mad about Maths

mathematical games

CW00406186

Adrian & Jeni Pinel

ReD KiTE

Welcome to Mad About Maths: Mathematical Games!

We all love games – they're exciting, fun and great to play again and again. But did you know that almost all games are based on numbers? Some games in this book are hundreds of years old and others are brand new. Some you'll know already, and others, from countries far away, you might not.

Each double page has a different mathematical theme on it for you to get to grips with. Follow the instructions carefully on how to play the games or solve each puzzle. Keep an eye out for 'info' boxes, handy hints and clues that will give you a bit of extra help along the way.

At the back of this book, you'll find a 12-page section full of different games pieces and boards for you to use for the games. For example, take a look at the game called Multiple Choices on page 15. As well as needing two dice, each player will also need a copy of the Multiple Choices game board. Turn to the back section and find the right board – everything is labelled so you shouldn't have any problems finding it. First, photocopy the board – you may want to use it again, change its size or give a copy to a friend so they can play their own games at home, too. Then play the game, writing numbers in the spaces on the game board following the instructions on the page.

Above all, have fun with this book!

5 6 7 8 9 10

Contents

Three in a Row .4

Trapped! 6

Polish Puzzlers 8

The Jersey Game 10

Down to One 12

Fun with Factors 14

Play your Cards Right 16

Dominoes 18

Fair and Square 20

Collect a Set 22

In a Loop 24

Number Boxes 26

Stay on Track 28

Have a Guess 30

Answers 32

mathematical games
Three in a Row

Nine Men's Morris was a very popular game in England during the reign of Elizabeth I, and it is still played today, hundreds of years later. It's all about moving counters to make lines of three – sounds simple, but you have to keep your wits about you if you want to win!

Nine Men's Morris

This is a game for two players and is played on a square board like the one shown here. Each player starts with nine playing counters, which are called merels.

You take turns to place one counter at a time on the board. When all the counters are on the board, you can move them by sliding along lines into another space. When you make a line of three of your own counters, you can remove one of the other player's counters from the board.

To win
Reduce your opponent's counters to just two.

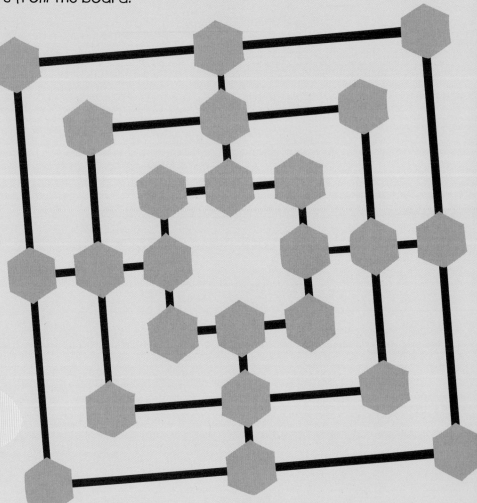

Use the game board provided with this book to play the game.

Mastering merels

Although the nine merels game is most people's favourite, there are some other versions that you can play. They all have the same rules – it's just the number of counters and the board that changes.

Three Merels

Each player has three counters. The simplest merel game – a good one to begin with!

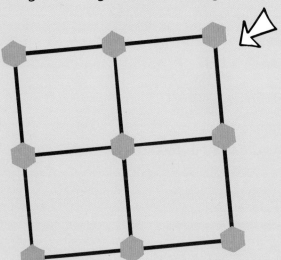

Six Merels

The players have six counters each. This game needs more strategy!

Try playing each merels game a few times to get an idea of good moves and strategies.

Merel peril

What would you do in these two situations?

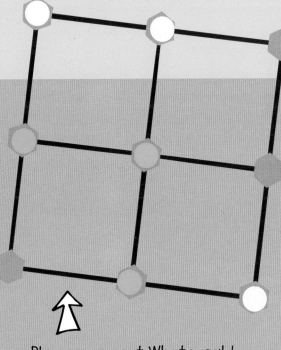

Blue moves next. What would be a good move?

Yellow moves next.

mathematical games
Trapped!

In these traditional games for two players one player tries to trap the other. You have to plan your moves carefully to avoid getting caught!

Ka'u'a

Ka'u'a is about a contest between a tiger and seven members of the Ka'u'a tribe. The tribe try to trap the tiger, but the tiger tries to catch them – one by one! This game is played on a star-shaped board – you can use the one provided. One player is the trapper and starts with seven playing pieces – the Ka'u'a – placed as shown on this board. The other player is the hunted tiger and has one playing piece that can be placed in any of the three remaining spaces. So you need seven counters of one colour and one of another colour.

You take turns to move. The trapper makes the first move, sliding one of his Ka'u'a along a line into an empty space. The tiger can move either by moving along a line into an empty space or by leaping over a Ka'u'a into an empty space. A Ka'u'a that the tiger leaps over is 'caught' and removed from the board. If there is space to do so, the tiger can make two or more leaps in a single turn!

Try playing the game a few times to get an idea of good moves.

To win
The tiger wins if it catches three of the Ka'u'a.

The Ka'u'a win if the tiger is trapped and unable to move.

On the spot
What would you do next in these two situations?

You are the tiger. You have already caught one Ka'u'a, so there are six left. It's your move.

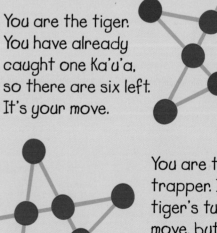

You are the trapper. It's the tiger's turn to move, but there is only one possible move it can make, so you can plan your next move. What should it be?

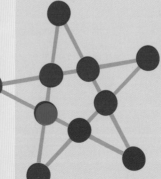

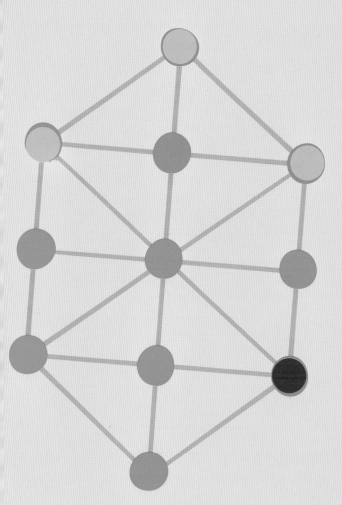

Hare and Hounds

Hare and Hounds is a traditional English game. The trapper has three playing pieces – the hounds – placed as shown on the board. The hare has one playing piece that can be placed in any other space. You need three counters of one colour and one of another colour.

You take turns to move. The trapper makes the first move, sliding one of his hounds along a line into an empty space – he is not allowed to move hounds backwards, but he can move them sideways. The hare can move in any direction.

To win

The hare wins if it escapes past the hounds to the top of the board.

The hounds win if the hare is trapped and unable to move.

Stuck

The name of this game is exactly what you are when you are trapped – stuck! Both players have five playing pieces placed as shown on the board.

You take turns to move, sliding one of your pieces forwards or backwards into an empty space – never sideways or diagonally. In each move, you can move either one or two spaces along.

To win

The winner is the first one to trap the other player's counters so that there is nowhere to move them.

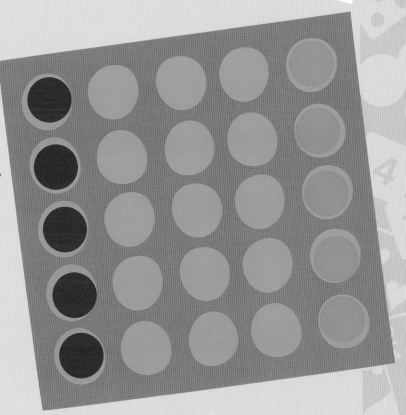

mathematical games
Polish Puzzlers

These two games are based on traditional games from Poland. Both games use dice, and winning depends on how you use the score you throw – it definitely helps if you can add and multiply! So get out the game boards provided and get the dice rolling!

Crossing the River

The aim of this game is to get your playing pieces across the river before anyone else.

To win

Be the first player to get four of your counters across the river.

Each player needs six counters in one colour. First decide which side of the river you will start from. Then take turns to place each of your counters beside a number on the riverbank. More than one counter can be placed beside the same number. When all the counters have been placed, take turns to throw two dice and find their total. If one of your counters is beside that total, it can 'cross the river'. So, if you have thrown numbers that add up to six, and you have a counter beside six on the riverbank, it can go across. Only one counter can cross the river for any one throw. If you get a counter across the river, you get another throw. Otherwise it is the next player's turn.

The Calculations Game

In this game you need to use your calculating skills and strategy to get the highest score. You need ten counters for each player – each player has a different colour – and three dice. Take turns to throw the dice. You have to use the three numbers thrown to reach a number on the board, where you can place one of your counters.

For example, if you've thrown 🎲, 🎲 and 🎲, you could simply do some adding and subtracting:

🎲 + 🎲 − 🎲 = 1

🎲 + 🎲 − 🎲 = 5

🎲 + 🎲 − 🎲 = 7

🎲 + 🎲 + 🎲 = 13

Or you could bring in some multiplication too:

[🎲 + 🎲] × 🎲 = 42   [🎲 + 🎲] × 🎲 = 36   [🎲 + 🎲] × 🎲 = 30

[🎲 × 🎲] + 🎲 = 18   [🎲 × 🎲] + 🎲 = 22   [🎲 × 🎲] + 🎲 = 27

[🎲 × 🎲] − 🎲 = 6   [🎲 × 🎲] − 🎲 = 14   [🎲 × 🎲] − 🎲 = 21

The board shows numbers 1 to 100 in a 10×10 grid.

Scoring Key

Colour	Points	Colour	Points	Colour	Points
■	13	■	9	■	6
■	12	■	8	■	5
■	11	■	7	■	1

How does the Scoring Key work?

To win

Add up the points you've scored at the end of the game. The player with the highest score wins.

Choose one of your totals and place your counter on that number.

You can't place your counter on a space occupied by someone else's counter, but you can put more than one of your own counters on the same number.

The colours on the board and the scoring key show that some numbers will score more points than others. So if you cover the number 65, you score 13 points, but 75 will score only 5 points. The game ends when all the counters are on the board.

mathematical games
The Jersey Game

Numero is a dice game that is more than 150 years old. It's also known as The Jersey Game because it was invented on the island of Jersey. These versions of Numero can be played by two or more players. You could even play them on your own like a game of Patience.

Numero

This is a game for two players. You need two ordinary dice. You can easily make your own game board. It looks like this:

Each player has five turns, unless the game ends before that! In each turn you throw the dice, add the numbers to get a total and then cover any numbers on the board that make that total. Here's an example:

You throw

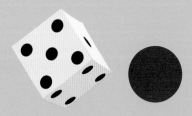 **= 8**

You may cover any numbers that total 8, if they are not already covered – 1 and 7, 2 and 6, 3 and 5, or 1, 3 and 4.

Keep throwing the dice until you can't make a total from the remaining numbers on the board. Then your turn is over. Add up the remaining numbers as your score for that turn. Now it's the other player's turn so remove all your counters from the board – each turn starts with a clear board. After five turns each, add up your scores. The player with the lowest score wins the game.

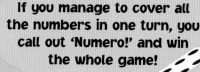

If you manage to cover all the numbers in one turn, you call out 'Numero!' and win the whole game!

Twelves Numero

This is also a game that can be played by two players or teams, but the board and the dice are different. You need one ordinary dice and another dice with the numbers 4 to 9 on it. (If you haven't got one, make one by putting sticky paper numbers on an ordinary dice.)

The game is played like basic Numero, except that this time you can decide on any of three ways of getting a total from the numbers you throw. Here's an example:

You throw

 and

You can use that as 11 (4 + 7) or 3 (7 – 4) or 28 (4 x 7).

You must say how you got your total each time, before you cover a number.

Run For Cover!

This version uses the same board as Twelves Numero and can be played by two teams as well as two players. The game starts with all the even numbers on the board covered. Whoever starts tries to cover all the odd numbers using the total thrown on the dice. You can continue throwing until you can't use your full total to cover the numbers. The next player then has to try to uncover the numbers – both odd and even. The winner is the player who covers or uncovers all the numbers in one turn.

mathematical games
Down to One

Some games involve removing counters from a board, according to the rules of the game, until there is just one single – solitary – counter left! That's how Solitaire got its name. In Solitaire puzzles and games, counters are removed by another counter jumping over them into an empty space. Here are some brain-teasing versions for you to try!

Star Solitaire

Place nine counters on the star as shown. Make 'jump and removal' moves until there is only one counter remaining. A series of jumps into several empty spaces is counted as just one move!

- Does the last counter always land on the same space?

- Does it always take the same number of moves to complete the puzzle?

- What is the minimum possible number of moves?

Try starting the puzzle with the empty space on one of the points of the star.

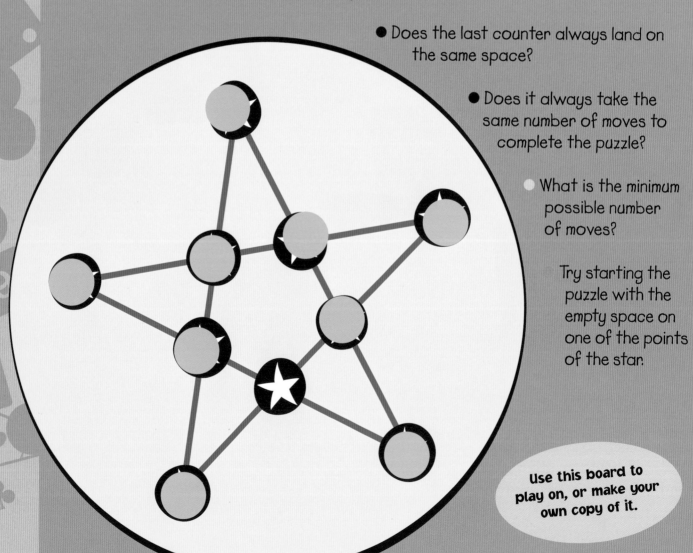

Use this board to play on, or make your own copy of it.

Cross Solitaire

Start with eight counters on this cross, leaving the centre space empty.

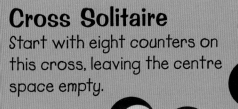

Try the same puzzle with the larger cross. How many counters are you left with this time?

Use these crosses to play a game for two players by taking turns to make moves, until one of you cannot move and loses the game!

- Is it possible to make 'jump and removal' moves until there are only three counters left?

- What about just two counters left?

- Is it possible to have just one left?

Use the board provided to play the game.

Maltese Cross

Now that you've had some practice, here's something to work your brain a little harder!

This time you need 31 counters because there are 32 spaces on the board. A good place to leave the empty space is in the very middle of the board, as shown. Try to make 'jump and removal' moves until there is only one counter remaining. Keep a check on the number of counters you are left with at the end each time – note down your lowest amount, until you manage to end with just one!

Here's a really tough challenge: can you make the last counter end up in the centre?

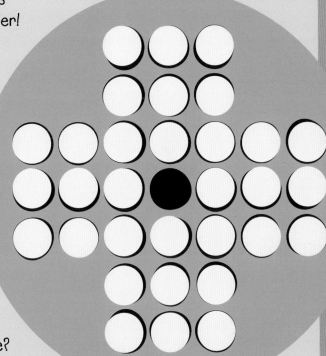

mathematical games
Fun With Factors

These games are about finding factors and making choices – knowing your times tables will definitely be an advantage!
Two or more players can play. Use the blank game boards provided to make boards like these.

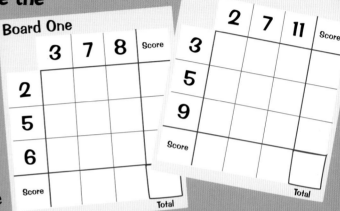

Multiple Choices

You need two dice, and each player needs a copy of the same board.
Choose one dice to represent the first digit of a number, and the other to represent the second – you throw these dice in turn to make a two-digit number.
So, if you throw 5 with the first dice and 4 with the second, the number is 54.

Take turns throwing the dice. Each player must write the two-digit number in one of the spaces on their board. Choose carefully! You score a point if the number is a multiple of either of the set numbers above and to the left of the space you choose. If it is a multiple of both, you score two points. For example, on Board One, the best place for 54 would be in the 3 column and the 6 row, because 54 is a multiple of both 3 and 6.

When all the spaces are filled, check the points scores of each row and column, then add these together to get your total. The winner is the player with the highest total.

Example: on Board One

	3	7	8	Score
2	44	21	32	2
5	15	35	16	2
6	54	42	24	3
Score	2	3	3	15 (Total)

Here's an example of how a game might end using Board One:

In the rows:
- 44 and 32 are multiples of 2
- 15 and 35 are multiples of 5
- 54, 42 and 24 are all multiples of 6

In the columns:
- 15 and 54 are multiples of 3
- 21, 35 and 42 are all multiples of 7
- 32, 16 and 24 are all multiples of 8

7 points from the rows and 8 from the columns give a total of 15.

Warp Factor Nine

For this game you need just one dice and are looking for factors. Here are some boards for the game. You could make up your own too, using numbers that have lots of factors

As before, each player needs a copy of the same board for the game. Take turns to throw the dice. Each player must write the number thrown in one of the spaces on their board. You score a point if that number is a factor of either of the numbers above and to the left of that space. If it is a factor of both numbers, you score two points.

So, on Board One, the best place for 5 would be in the 30 column and the 10 row, because 5 is a factor of both 30 and 10. On Board Two, the best place would be in the 20 column and the 10 row.

When all nine spaces are filled, check the points scores of each row and column, then add these together to get your total. The winner is the player with the highest total.

Board One

	9	18	30	Score
10				
16				
36				
Score				

Board Two

	12	20	36	Score
10				
15				
24				
Score				Total

If you can, use dice with numbers on them rather than dots.

Here's an example of how a game might end using Board One:

Example: on Board One

	9	18	30	Score
10	3	6	5	1
16	2	4	1	3
36	3	6	4	3
Score	2	2	2	15 Total

In the rows:
    5 is a factor of 10
    1, 2 and 4 are all factors of 16
    3, 4 and 6 are all factors of 36

In the columns:
    3 is a factor of 9, and there are two of them
    6 is a factor of 18, and there are two of them
    5 and 1 are factors of 30

7 points from the rows and 6 from the columns makes a total of 13.

Now try making some game boards of your own!

mathematical games
Play Your Cards Right

Now you can brush up your mathematical skills while you enjoy a game of cards! In some games you have to work out how likely you are to get a particular card so that you can decide what to do next. In other games you have to collect cards that will add up to a particular score to win the game.

Twenty-One

Twenty-One is a card game for two or more players. You need a pack of standard playing cards. Each card has a value from 1 to 10, including the Jack, Queen and King cards which all count as 10. But aces are special – they count as 1 or 11. Shuffle the pack and deal out two cards to each player. Cards are placed face up on the table. You add the numbers on your cards and each player says their total. Whoever has the smallest total takes another card from the pack and says their new total. The player with the next smallest total does the same. Play continues like this. If a player gets a total of more than 21, they have to drop out. This continues until there is just one player left. That player wins the round and gets 2 points. But if any player reaches exactly 21 at any time during the game, they win the round immediately and score 5 points.

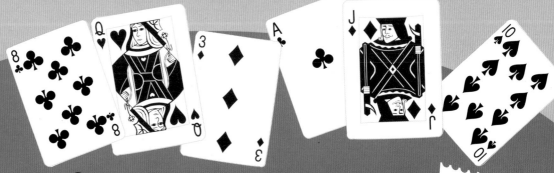

Fifty-One

Fifty-One is the same kind of game as Twenty-One, except that the target total is 51. And some of the cards have different values – Jack counts as 12, Queen as 14, King as 16, ace as 20. The winner of a round scores 4 points – and an exact 51 scores 10 points.

Fifteens

Fifteens is a game for two players. You need a line of playing cards like this – an ace counts as 1:

Take turns to pick a card. To win the game you must be the first player to have any cards that add up to exactly 15, so choose carefully!

Here's an example:

You pick   The other player picks

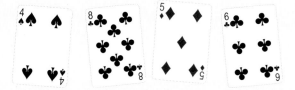   

You win because 4 + 5 + 6 = 15. The fact that you also have the 8 does not matter.

Target

Target is also a game for two players. You need a counter each and two lines of playing cards each, laid out as in Fifteens. You also need a number track like this one. Use the cards provided to make it:

35	36	37	38	39	40	41	42	43	44	45	46	47	48	49	50
34															

33	32	31	30	29	28	27	26	25	24	23	22	21	20	19	18

17

1	2	3	4	5	6	7	8	9	10	11	12	13	14	15	16

For each game, pick a number in the top row as the finishing line. You take turns to pick a playing card from your line – after you choose a card, turn it over so that it isn't used again. The player who starts moves their counter to the corresponding number in the number track. Then the other player picks one of their cards and adds that number to the first, placing their counter on the new total. The first player picks another number, adds it, and moves their counter. And so the game continues. The winner is the first to go past the finishing line – past the chosen number!

mathematical games

Dominoes

These two domino games can be played by two to four players. If there are four players, you could form two teams!

Take Five

Take Five is quite like ordinary dominoes, except for the way it is scored. Spread out a set of dominoes face down on the table and mix them up to make the 'pool'. Each player takes five dominoes from the pool. If anyone has the double five, they start the game by placing it face up on the table, scoring 2 points.

If none of you has the double five, each player takes a domino from the pool in turn until one of you picks it up.

Players take turns to place a domino that matches one of the ends of the line, just as in ordinary dominoes. If you have not got a domino that matches, take another from the pool and wait for your next turn.

After each turn, add up the numbers at the ends of the lines. If your domino makes this total into a multiple of five, you score! If the total is 5, you score 1 point; if it is 10 (2 x 5), you score 2 points, if it is 15 (3 x 5), you score 3 points, and so on.

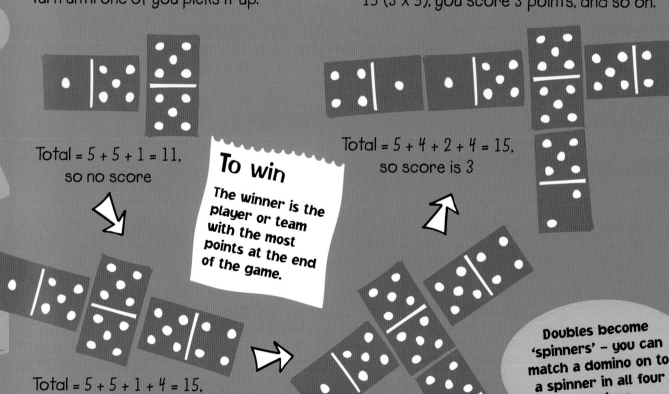

Total = 5 + 5 + 1 = 11, so no score

Total = 5 + 4 + 2 + 4 = 15, so score is 3

To win

The winner is the player or team with the most points at the end of the game.

Total = 5 + 5 + 1 + 4 = 15, so score is 3

Total = 5 + 1 + 2 + 4 = 12, so no score

Doubles become 'spinners' – you can match a domino on to a spinner in all four directions.

Try playing Take Four and Take Six – games that are just like Take Five except that four or six replaces five in all of the rules!

Domino End Game

Domino End Game is another variation of Take Five. In this game, any double domino can be used to start. Before the game, you must choose some numbers – multiples of these numbers will score points.

For example, you might decide on 3, 4 and 5.

The numbers at the ends are added up after each turn. If the total is a multiple of 3, you score 3, if it is a multiple of 4, you score 4, and so on.

Can you guess what you score when the total is 12? It's a multiple of 3 and a multiple of 4, so you score 3 + 4 = 7!

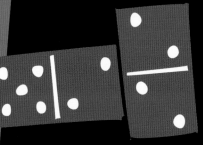

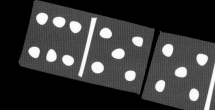

Total = 2 + 2 + 5 = 9, so the score is 3

Can you work out the score for this?

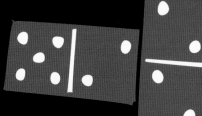

Total = 2 + 2 + 5 + 6 = 15, so the score is 5 + 3 = 8

To win

The winner is the player or team with the most points at the end of the game.

mathematical games
Fair and Square

Many games are played on a square board divided into squares, such as draughts or chess which are played on a chequered square board. These two games are simpler than chess, but you do have to think carefully about where to place your counters!

Square Dance

This is a game for two to four players – four players can play in two teams.

Take turns placing a counter of your chosen colour on the board. When someone places a counter that completes the four corners of a square in their own colour – they win! Try blocking other players' squares to stop them winning!

Use the game board provided to play the game.

Here's a game that is about to end. Red to play. Where could you place a counter to win the game?

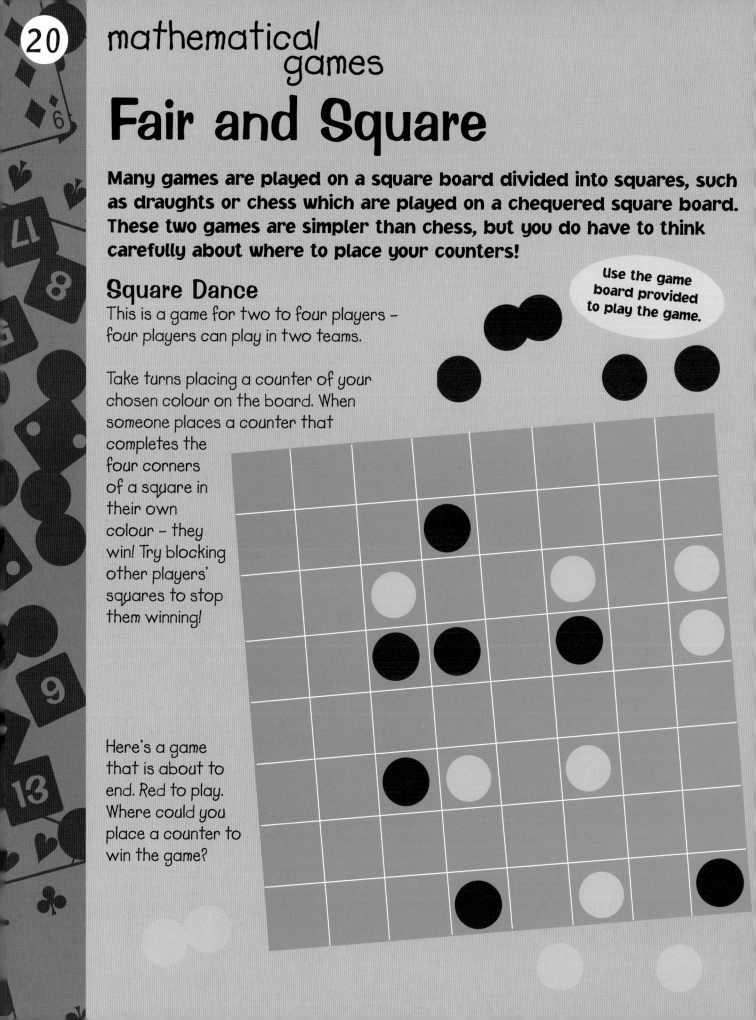

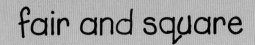

Line of Three

For Line of Three, you need a square board with 36 spaces. You can make one using the board for Square Dance – just make a copy and mask off the outer squares using paper and sticky tape.

Take turns placing a counter on the board. If someone places a counter that completes a straight line of three of any colour – they lose! The counters don't need to be next to each other to make the line.

Here's a game about to end. Is there somewhere to place your counter where you would not lose the game? Which spaces are the ones where you would definitely lose?

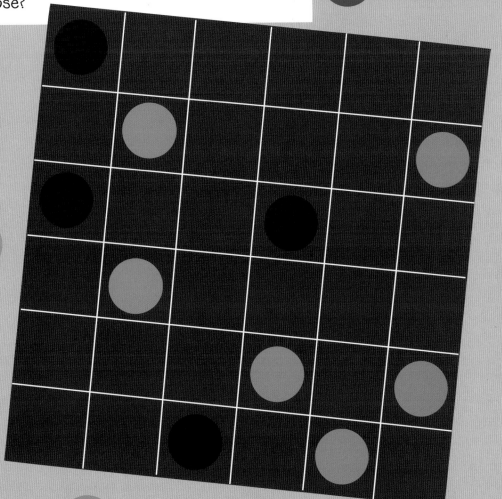

mathematical games
Collect a Set

These card games are a fun way of practising calculations! You'll need a set of Number cards and Function cards. There are templates provided that you can photocopy and use to make the cards. You'll need to enlarge them when you copy them.

The Input-Output Game
This is a game for two to four players – if there are four players, they can form two teams.

The aim of the game is to collect Trios – sets of three cards:
- The first card is the Input – a Number card.
- The second card is the Function – a Function card.
- The last card is the Output – a Number card.

For example:

3   x 4, – 1   =   11

Separate the cards into two packs – Numbers and Functions – and shuffle them. Each player takes two Function cards and four Number cards from the packs. This leaves a pack of Number cards and a pack of Function cards which you draw from as the game continues.

Look at your cards carefully – can you make a Trio? If you can, when it is your turn, place your Trio on the table in front of you, and then take two Number cards and one Function card from the packs to replace them.

x 2, + 1
x 2, – 1
x 2, + 3
x 3, + 1
x 3, – 1
x 2
x 4, – 1
x 4, + 3
x 5
x 5, – 1
x 2, + 5
x 3
x 4, + 2
x 4, + 1
x 3, + 2
x 2, + 2
x 3, + 4
x 4

If you can't make a Trio, you pick up an extra card from one of the two packs to add to your cards.

When there are no more cards in the packs, and no one can put a Trio on the table, the game is over and it's time to count your scores. You score the sum of all the number cards in your Trios. The player or the team with the highest score wins!

Trios can be challenged by other players. If you think it doesn't work – say so!

Strings

Here's another version of the Input-Output Game – it's called Strings. The rules are the same, except that after a Trio is put down on the table, any player can add to it at either end.

For example:
Someone has put down a Trio:

$$5 \quad \times 2 \quad = \quad 10$$

It could be added to at one end like this:

$$2 \quad \times 3, -1 \quad = \quad 5 \quad \times 2 \quad = \quad 10$$

Or at the other end like this:

$$5 \quad \times 2 \quad = \quad 10 \quad \times 2, +1 \quad = \quad 21$$

Strings can grow longer and longer during the game. Remember that you can put down a new Trio instead of adding to a String.

The winner is the first player to use up all the cards in their hand.

mathematical games

In a Loop

Playing this game could seriously improve your calculating skills! Each time you play the game, the calculations come out in a different order. You'll find you get quicker at doing them the more you play!

Card Calculations

Look at these eight cards. They are all in Set A – there's an A in the top right-hand corner of each card.

20 A
– 15

5 A
x 3

15 A
– 12

3 A
x 8

10 A
x 2

40 A
– 30

4 A
x 10

24 A
– 20

Choose any card and do the calculation on it. Find your answer on the top corner of another card. Pick that card and do the calculation. What happens when you continue doing this? When you get to the last card and do the calculation, where is the answer? Can you see why these cards are called Loop Cards?

Use the templates provided to make this set and the other three sets of Loop Cards. Do all the sets of eight cards make a loop?

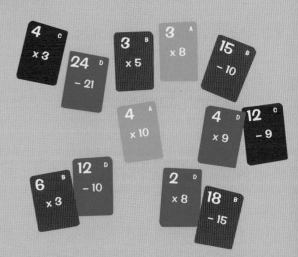

The Loop Cards Game

Now you are ready to play a Loop Cards game. The game can be played by two to four players. If there are four of you, use all four sets of cards. If there are three, you need three of the sets, and so on. Shuffle all the cards together and deal them out to the players so that you each hold the same number of cards. Decide who is going to start, then take turns to put down cards. To play your turn you must hold a card that has the answer to the last card put down. Otherwise you miss your turn.

For example:
The first player
puts down

So the next card has to
be one of these:

The first player to use up all their cards is the winner. But you can carry on playing to see if all the cards can be played out, with the last card's answer being on the first card played. This is a way of checking that no mistakes were made in the game. Sometimes a few cards are left over at the end of a game. Check that they make a little loop or loops.

Here's an example of how a game may progress. What should the number at the top of the next card be?

20 A
− 15

5 B
x 4

20 C
− 16

4 D
x 9

36 D
− 30

4 C
x 3

24 A
− 20

6 D
X 4

mathematical games
Number Boxes

Have you ever played the 'Boxes' game where you mark out squares of dots on paper and then take turns to join them up to make squares? It's a traditional pastime that people have enjoyed for many years. You can make it even more fun by adding numbers!

Dots galore

You can play the basic game on a dot grid like this one.
Make copies of this to play the game on.

You need two players or two teams. There are only a few rules to remember:

- In each turn, you draw a line joining two dots to make part of a square or 'box'.
- If this completes a box, it is yours, so you put your mark or colour in it to claim it.
- If you complete a box, you must draw another line – sometimes this leads to a whole chain of boxes being completed!

> Putting numbers in the grid makes the game more interesting!
>
> The rules are exactly the same, except that when you claim a box, you score the points shown by its number.

Look at the numbers on these grids. Find the totals of each row and each column. What do you notice? Now find the total of each little square of four numbers. There is a Key number for each grid. What is the total of all the numbers on the grid? Can you see how it's connected to the Key number? This can help you to keep track of your score during the game!

Make copies of these two grids and challenge a friend to a Number Box Game!

14	32	20	34
51	3	45	1
26	30	22	22
9	35	13	43

7	4	12	2
7	7	2	9
3	8	8	6
8	6	3	8

Puzzling grids

Imagine that it is your turn to play.
- Can you win from this position?
- What should you do next?
- What are the scores at the end of each game, if you play your best moves?

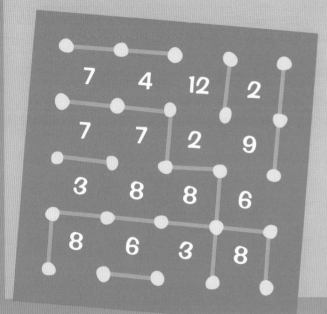

Try making some game grids of your own. First, choose a Key number for each row, column and block of four numbers – for example, 80. The average number will be 80 divided by 4 – that's 20.

You can pick any numbers to go in the first three places of the top row of the grid, but the last number in that row must make the total up to your Key number.

You can pick the first number in each of the next two rows. Then you can calculate what other numbers are needed to make the total up to the Key number for each block of four, each row and each column.

Congratulations! You have made your own Number Boxes Game grid!!

Here's another game grid. What is its Key number?

mathematical games
Stay on Track

Making Tracks is a game that tests your skills of mental calculation and strategy. Winning or losing depends on how the three dice fall and on your strategic choice when you have one. Other players may block you. Can you stay on track to win the game?

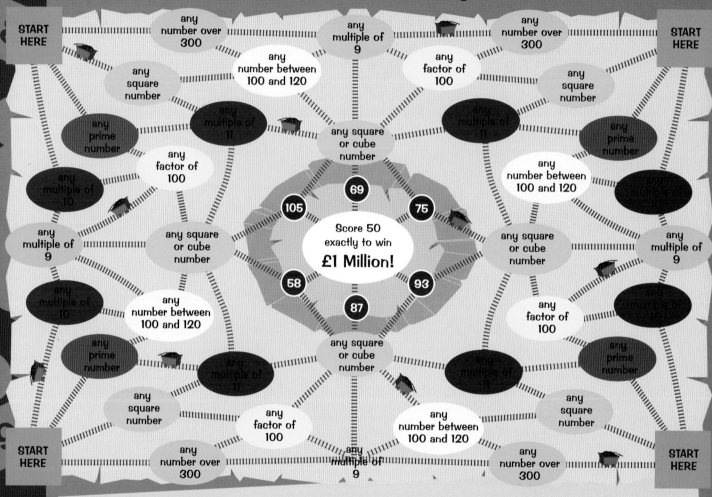

Making Tracks
This game is for two to four players. There are four starting places on the board. You need an ordinary dice and two specially numbered dice:

The first dice is numbered 1 2 3 4 5 6

The second dice is numbered 4 5 6 7 8 9

The third dice is numbered 7 8 9 10 11 12

To win
Be the first to reach the £1 million space

Use the game board provided to play the game.

- First, you all choose a place to start. You need to move about the board to get nearer to the million or to block other players.

- You take turns to throw all three dice. Try to use all three numbers you throw to make a number that fits into a neighbouring space.

- No player can move on to an occupied space.

- You can only move to one of the neighbouring spaces each time.

You may have choices of where to move!

For example:
If you are at a starting place and throw

 , and **8**

you could add all three to get 19, which is a prime number.

Or you could multiply 7 x 8 = 56, then add the 4 to get 60, which is a multiple of 10.

Or you could multiply 8 x 4 = 32, then subtract 7 to get 25, which is a square number.

That gives you at least three directions you could go away from the start.

Rules for moving to spaces on the board

To move from your Start Space you need to get a number that is one of these:
- A multiple of 10
  A Prime Number
- A Square Number
- More than 300

To move to spaces between Start Spaces and Access Points you need to get a number that is one of these:
- A multiple of 11
- A multiple of 9
- A factor of 100
- A Cube Number
- Between 100 and 120

To move to an Access Point you need a Square or Cube number.

In the Central Area you must make specific numbers in each case – the six places surrounding the centre are:

69   93   58

75   87   105

To land on the central spot you must get exactly 50 – then you've won £1 million!

There are lots of ways you can vary the rules after you've played the game a few times.

mathematical games
Have a Guess

Have you ever had to think about how wide or how long something is? You might have wondered whether the game you got for your birthday will fit on your shelf, or whether your new poster will fit in that space between the cupboard and the window. These games will brush up your estimating skills!

In-Between

In-Between is a game for two teams, or two players. You'll need some measuring equipment – tape measure, ruler, measuring jug, weighing scales – depending on what you choose to measure during the game.

In each round, each team secretly selects an object in the room that can be measured in some way with the equipment available. Then the teams tell each other what the objects are. Neither team is allowed to go near the objects at this stage.

Each team secretly discusses estimates of the measurements. After an agreed time – for example, three minutes – the teams must write their estimate on a piece of paper. But it must be two measurements 'In-Between' which you are sure the actual measurement will be.

Now measure the object. Teams should agree on who will check the actual measurement.

- If only one team 'captures' the actual measurement within their two estimated measures, they win!
- If neither team captures the measurement, no one wins.
- If both teams capture the measurement, the team with the smaller gap wins!

For example, your team might estimate the height of a table as being between 60cm and 80cm – a gap of 20cm.
The other team might decide it is between 70cm and 100cm – a gap of 30cm.
- If the height of the table is actually 69cm, your team wins.
- If it is 84cm, the other team wins.
- If it is 75cm, both teams have captured the measurement, but your team wins as it had a smaller gap of 20cm instead of 30cm.

Mental Maths

Here's another version of the In-Between game. You'll need two sets of digit cards from 0 to 9 – you can use the ones from the Numbers set – and a calculator for checking answers – but don't use it for the first part of the game!

In each round, each team takes turns to select four digit cards from a shuffled pack. They are fitted in order into these spaces:

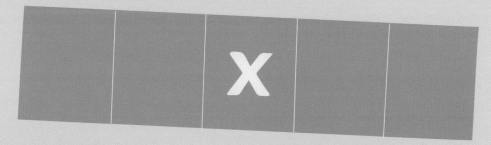

So, for example, you may get this:

Each team secretly discusses their estimates of the result of this calculation. Remember, you can't use a calculator or a pen and paper! After an agreed time – for example, one minute – the teams must write their estimate on a piece of paper. But it must be two numbers 'In-Between' which you are sure the actual answer will be.

Now check the multiplication using the calculator. The teams should agree on who will do this.

- If only one team 'captures' the answer within their two estimated numbers, they win!
- If neither team captures the answer, no-one wins.
- If both teams capture the answer, the team with the smaller gap wins!

There are lots of variations on this game. Try making up some yourself!

Answers

pages 4–5 Three in a Row

Merel peril

Blue should move the central counter to the middle position on the right. This blocks the yellow counter moving there – after that it could have been moved to a winning position.

Yellow should move the counter on the inner square down one space. This puts it in position to move to the right to complete a line of three in the next turn. Blue needs two moves to complete a line, so Yellow will get there first and can remove a blue counter – the one that could make Blue's line of three.

pages 6–7 Trapped!

On the Spot

You are the tiger. You can catch three Ka'u'a by leaping over them as shown here. So you win the game.

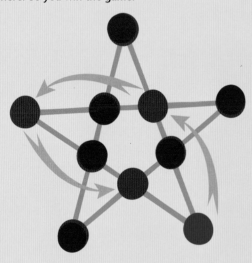

You are the trapper. The tiger has moved to the only place it can. Now you can move as shown here. This will force the tiger into a corner. After that there are only a couple of moves left until the tiger is trapped!

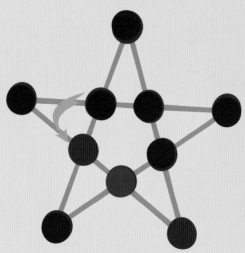

pages 8–9 Polish Puzzlers

The Calculations Game

The colours on the board correspond with the colour of the numbers in the Scoring Key. All multiples of 13 are coloured in red, and you score 13 points if you place your counter on a red number. Multiples of 12 and 11 are coloured in blue and light green, so you score 12 points on a blue number and 11 on a light green one. Then, missing out 10, multiples of 9 are coloured in pink. But 99 is already coloured for 11 so it is left as light green. After the multiples of 8, 7, 6 and 5 are coloured in using the same method, all the remaining spaces are made dark green to show they are worth just 1 point.

pages 18–19 Dominoes

The third score for the Domino End Game is 4 because the total = 2 + 2 + 6 + 6 = 16, a multiple of 4.

pages 20–21 Fair and Square

Square Dance

Placing the counter as shown will complete a square and win the game.

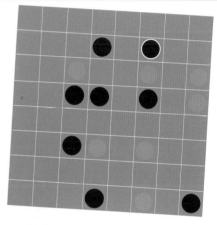

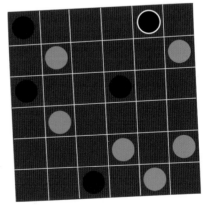

Line of Three

There is only one safe square to place your counter. If you place it on any of the other squares, it will complete a line of three.

pages 24–25 In a Loop

The Loops Cards Game

The number at the top of the next card should be 12.

pages 26–27 Number Boxes

Dots galore

The Key numbers for the grids are 25 and 100.

Puzzling grids

The Key number for the game grid is 10.

Ka'u'a game board
(page 6)

Press-out counters to use
for the games

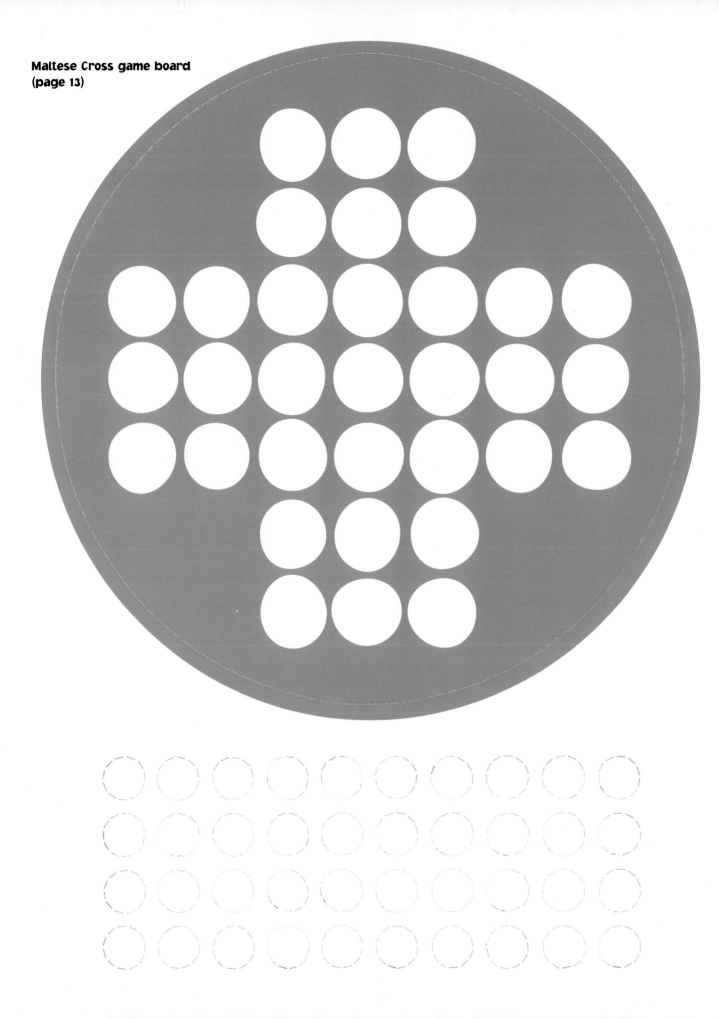

Maltese Cross game board
(page 13)

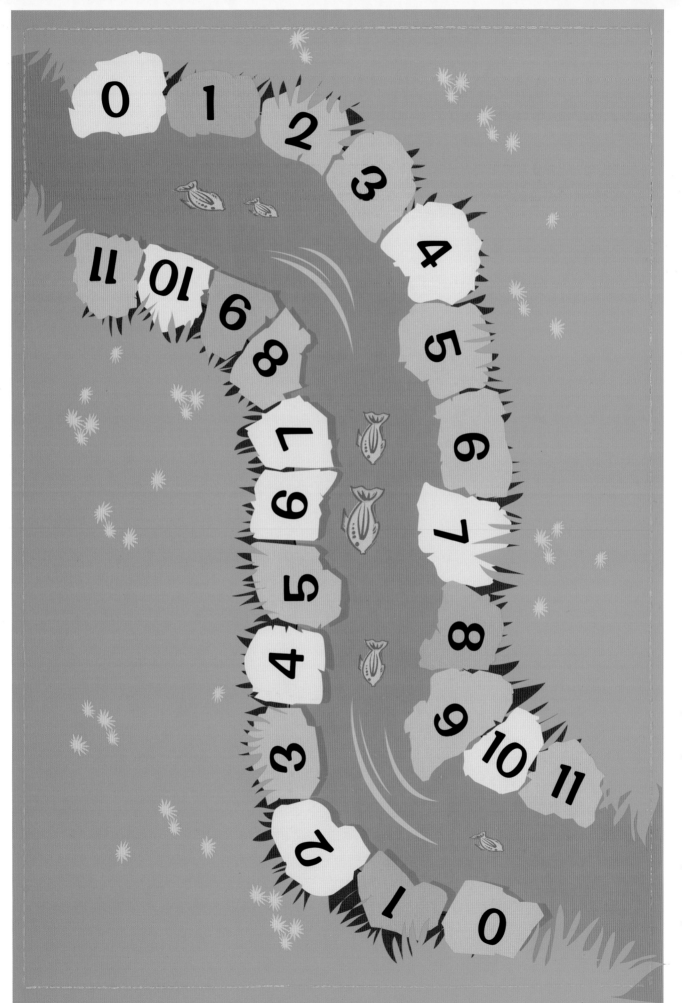

Crossing the River game board (page 8)

Making Tracks game board (page 28)

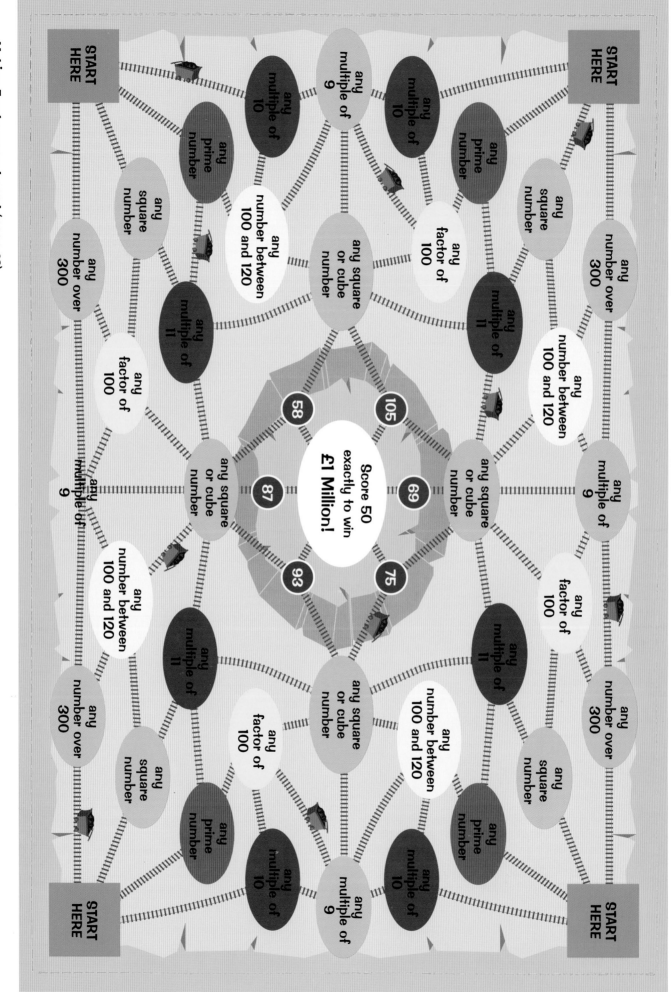

The Calculations Game game board (page 9)

1	2	3	4	5	6	7	8	9	10
11	12	13	14	15	16	17	18	19	20
21	22	23	24	25	26	27	28	29	30
31	32	33	34	35	36	37	38	39	40
41	42	43	44	45	46	47	48	49	50
51	52	53	54	55	56	57	58	59	60
61	62	63	64	65	66	67	68	69	70
71	72	73	74	75	76	77	78	79	80
81	82	83	84	85	86	87	88	89	90
91	92	93	94	95	96	97	98	99	100

Scoring Key

■ 13 ■ 12 ■ 11 ■ 9 □ 8 ■ 7 ■ 6 ■ 5 ■ 1

Square Dance game board (page 20)

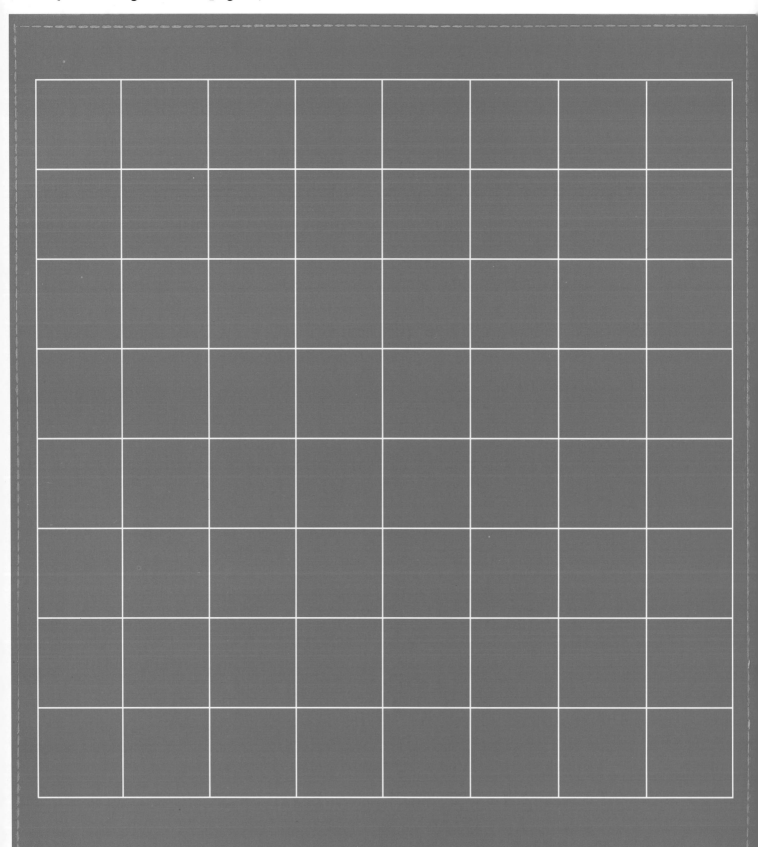

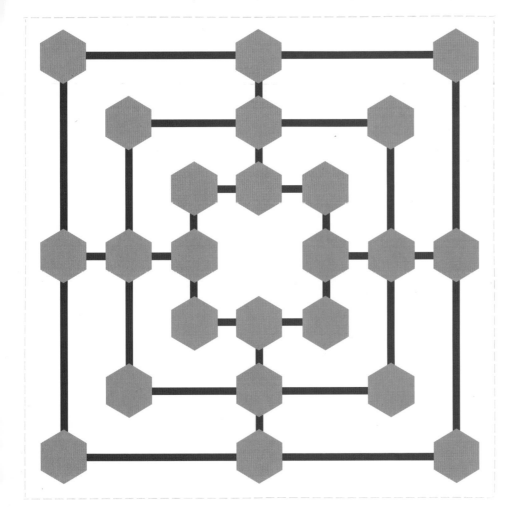

Nine Men's Morris game board (page 4)

Press-out counters to use for the games

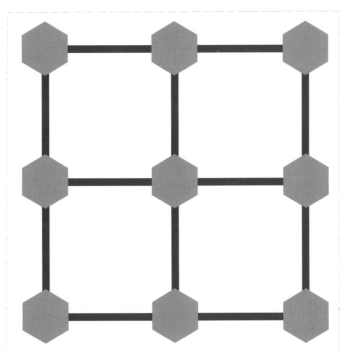

Three Merels game board (page 5)

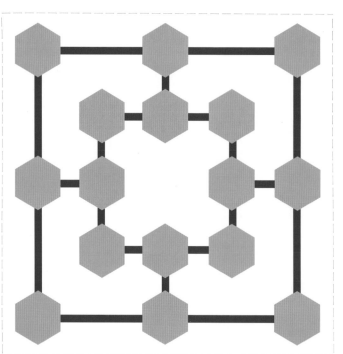

Six Merels game board (page 5)

Game boards for Multiple Choices and Warp Factor Nine games (pages 14-15)
Photocopy these to use for the games.

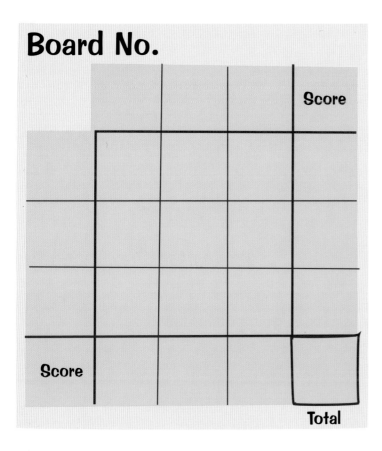

Board No.

Score

Score

Total

Board No.

Score

Score

Total

× 2, + 1

× 2, + 3

× 3, + 2

× 2, − 1

× 3, + 1

× 2, + 5

× 4, + 2

× 2, + 2

× 3, − 1

× 4, − 1

× 5

× 2

× 3, + 4

× 4

× 4, + 1

× 4, + 3

× 5, − 1

× 3

Function cards for the Input-
output Game and Strings
(pages 22-23)
Photocopy them. You can
enlarge them too and colour
them in.

20 A	5 A	15 A	20 B	2 B	12 B
− 15	x 3	− 12	− 18	x 6	− 6

3 A	24 A	4 A	6 B	18 B	3 B
x 8	− 20	x 10	x 3	− 15	x 5

40 A	10 A		15 B	5 B	
− 30	x 2		− 10	x 4	

20 C	4 C	12 C	6 D	24 D	3 D
− 16	x 3	− 9	x 4	− 21	x 4

3 C	21 C	7 C	12 D	2 D	16 D
x 7	− 14	x 2	− 10	x 8	− 12

14 C	2 C		4 D	36 D
− 12	x 10		x 9	− 30

Cards for the
Loop Cards Game
(pages 24-25)
Photocopy and enlarge
them. You can colour
each set (A, B, C and D)
a different colour after
you've copied them.

Number cards for the Input-Output Game and Strings (pages 22-23)
Photocopy and enlarge them. You can colour them in too.

1	2	3	4	5	6	7	8	9	10	11	12
13	14	15	16	17	18	19	20	21	22	23	24

Extra number cards for other games in this book

25	26	27	28	29	30	31	32	33	34	35	36	37
38	39	40	41	42	43	44	45	46	47	48	49	50

Dominoes templates (pages 18-19)

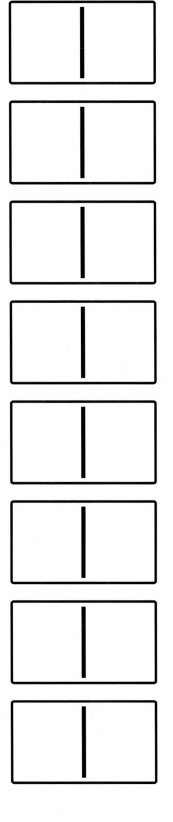